Follow the ants

by Brian Ogden

Bible stories for young readers

Acknowledgment

Mrs Gill Grainger, Head Teacher at Woolenwick First School in Stevenage, has made an invaluable contribution to this series by reading all the manuscripts and using the stories with her children.

Text copyright © 1999 Brian Ogden
Illustrations copyright © 1999 Simon Smith

The author asserts the moral right to
be identified as the author of this work

Published by
The Bible Reading Fellowship
Peter's Way, Sandy Lane West
Oxford OX4 5HG
ISBN 1 84101 077 4

First edition 1999

10 9 8 7 6 5 4 3 2 1 0

A catalogue record for this book is
available from the British Library

Printed and bound in Great Britain
by Caledonian International Book
Manufacturing Ltd, Glasgow

Introduction

This is the fifth in a series of books for children starting school. The setting is a reception class at Daisy Hill County Primary School. As with any classroom for younger children, the story mat is an important feature. The teacher, Mrs Jolley, relates the happenings in the classroom to stories from the Bible. It is hoped that teachers and parents will be able to choose stories which relate to their immediate circumstances and that the children will soon become friends with Mrs Jolley's children.

In each book there are seven stories, three from the Old Testament and four from the New. Bible references are given to enable the context of the story to be enlarged on if required. Prayers relating to each story are included for use in an assembly or with a story at bedtime. These are both to be found at the end of each book.

So please come now and meet Mrs Jolley, together with David, Emma, James, Sarah, Joshua and his twin sister Rosie, Michael, Hannah, Nathan and last, but not least, Sam. As it says on the classroom door...

Welcome to Mrs Jolley's Class

Contents

Feet first

It had been a busy morning
in Mrs Jolley's class.

Joshua and Hannah had been
cutting coloured shapes.

There were pieces of paper
on the chairs.

There were pieces of paper
on the floor.

There were even pieces of paper
in Joshua's hair!

Michael and Rosie had been working in the sand tray.

There was sand on the table.

There was sand on the floor.

There was sand on their clothes.

Emma and Nathan had been
colouring some pictures.

There were wax crayons
on the table.

One crayon rolled on to the floor.

The crayon broke into lots of pieces.

7

'Children,' said Mrs Jolley,
'stop what you are doing, please.

It is time to tidy up.

Put everything back
where you got it from.'

Joshua and Hannah carried on
talking to each other.

'I'm not going to pick up all
those bits,' said Joshua.

Michael and Rosie went to
wash their hands.

They didn't brush up the sand that
had fallen on the floor.

Emma and Nathan put their pictures
in their trays.

They left crayons lying on the table.

They left the crayon lying on the
floor.

The school bell rang. It was
lunch time.

The children went and had
their lunch.

When Joshua and Hannah came
back, they were surprised.

Their pieces of paper were still
on the floor.

Michael and Rosie were surprised.

The sand they had spilt was still
on the floor.

Emma and Nathan were surprised.

Their crayons had not been
put back in the box.

Mrs Jolley asked the children to sit
on the story mat.

'We had a busy morning this
morning,' she said.

'You worked with the sand, and with
the scissors and with the crayons.

But no one put anything away.

You all left it for someone else
to do.

I want to tell you a story
about Jesus.

It happened when Jesus had his
special meal with his friends.

In those days, everyone wore
sandals on their feet.

The roads were very dusty
when it was hot.

The roads were very muddy
when it was wet.

And everybody's feet got very,
very dirty.

Jesus put a towel round himself.
He filled a basin with some water.

Jesus knelt on the floor.

One by one, he washed the feet of
all his friends.

He dried them carefully on the
towel.

Jesus, who was God's Son,
did this for his friends.

He didn't think he was too great to
wash their feet. He just did it.'

Mrs Jolley looked at the children.

The children didn't look at Mrs Jolley.

It was quiet for a moment.

'Sorry we didn't clear up our cutting-out,' said Joshua.

'Sorry about the sand,' said Rosie.

'And sorry about the crayons,' said Emma and Nathan together.

A new school for Nathan

Nathan's mummy came to see Mrs Jolley after school one day.

Nathan played in the sand tray while his mummy and Mrs Jolley talked.

'I've come to tell you that we are moving,' said Nathan's mummy.

'Our new home is a long way away.

Nathan will have to go to a new school near our new home.'

'I'm very sorry to hear that,' said Mrs Jolley. 'The children will be sorry too.'

'We have sold our house
and we have to move very soon,'
said Nathan's mummy.

'Don't want to go,' said Nathan
in a loud voice.

Nathan looked as if he was
going to cry.

Nathan went home with his mummy.

The next day, after break,
Mrs Jolley asked the children to
sit on the story mat.

'Yesterday,' she said,
'Nathan's mummy told me that
the family is moving.

Nathan will be leaving Daisy Hill
and going to a new school.

Nathan is sad about it and so are we.

But sometimes we have to
leave our friends and our homes
and make new ones.

I want to tell you a story
about a man who left his friends
and his home.

His name was Abraham.
His wife's name was Sarah.

Abraham and Sarah didn't have
any children at that time.

They lived in a city called Haran.

One day God spoke to Abraham.

God told Abraham that he had to
leave Haran.

He had to leave his country.

He had to leave his father's home.

And he had to leave most of
his relations.

God told Abraham that he was going to a special land.

The land was called Canaan.

Abraham was seventy-five years old when he left.

I don't think Nathan is quite that old!

Abraham did what God wanted, and after a long journey they arrived in Canaan.

Abraham had lots of adventures in Canaan.

But all the time God was with him.

It must have been very hard
for Abraham to leave his home.

I'm sure that Abraham sent messages
back to his friends in Haran.

It is hard for us to have to
say goodbye to Nathan.

Perhaps we can send some messages
to him.

And perhaps he will send
some to us.

Maybe we could write to his
new school.

Nathan, we know you will be
very happy in your new school
but we shall miss you.'

All the children drew cards
for Nathan.

One by one, they came and gave
him their cards.

Nathan looked sad when
school finished.

Very soon, Mrs Jolley's class had a postcard.

It was from Nathan.

Nathan told them he was happy in his new school.

I'm the best!

'I'm best!' shouted David. 'I jumped further than you!'

Michael looked at David and shook his head.

'I'm best,' he said. 'I threw the ball furthest.'

'I'm best,' said Hannah. 'I skipped longer than you.'

The children were in the Big Hall.

They were doing PE.

'Well, I'm best 'cos I can run fastest,' said Joshua.

It seemed to be a
'being best at' morning.

Even back in the classroom
they were doing it.

'I'm the best reader,'
said Sarah.

'I'm best at drawing,'
said Rosie.

'And I'm best at painting,'
said Emma.

'I'm best at kicking,'
said Sam.

'And I'm the best teacher!'
said Mrs Jolley, laughing.

'Come on, all you "best ats",'
she said.

'Come and sit on the story mat.'

The best jumper and the best reader
sat down.

The best runner and the best kicker
sat down.

The best painter and the best
thrower sat down.

Soon everyone had sat down.

'We seem to be having a
funny morning,' said Mrs Jolley.

'Everyone seems to think that they
are the best at something.

We call this boasting.

It isn't very good to boast as
it makes you feel very important.

I want to tell you about some of
Jesus' friends.

Sometimes they thought that they
were very important.'

Just at that moment there was
a knock on the door.

It was Joshua's and Rosie's mummy.

She was holding baby Daniel's hand.

Daniel was Joshua's and Rosie's
little brother.

'May I borrow Daniel for a moment,
please?' asked Mrs Jolley.

Daniel toddled over to Mrs Jolley.

He took Mrs Jolley's hand and
smiled at all the children.

'Once, when the friends of Jesus
thought they were very important,
Jesus did a strange thing,'
said Mrs Jolley.

'He took a baby, just like Daniel, and
put the baby in front of them.

"The greatest in the Kingdom
of Heaven is the one who becomes
like a baby," said Jesus.

It was Jesus' way of telling us
that there are no "best ats".

He told us we should be like
a baby, who doesn't think he's best
at anything.'

'But I still think Daniel's
best at dribbling,'
said Rosie.

And everyone laughed,
especially Mrs Jolley.

Follow the ants

The children sat on the story mat.

Mrs Jolley sat in her chair.

On a small table by her side was a strange-looking box. The box was made of glass.

'This,' said Mrs Jolley, 'is a vivarium.

A vivarium is where we keep ants.

Because it is made of glass, we can see what the ants are doing.'

The children crowded closer and looked inside.

'I can see the ants,' said Emma.

'I can see lots of egg-things,' said Sam.

'Look,' said James, 'some of them are carrying bits and pieces.'

'Sit back for a moment,' said Mrs Jolley.

'You can all have a closer look later on.

But now it's time to do some work. Back to your tables, please.'

Soon all the children were back in their seats.

Michael and Sarah had their reading books.

Both of them were looking out of the window.

Hannah and Sam just sat talking to each other.

Rosie gave a big yawn… and then another one.

She and David were not doing their writing sheets.

Nobody was working hard at all.

It seemed to be a lazy day.

'Oh dear,' said Mrs Jolley, 'I think
we had better come back to the
story mat.'

The children sat down.

Mrs Jolley sat on her chair. The
vivarium with the ants was next to her.

Mrs Jolley had the big class Bible
in her hands.

'In the Bible,' said Mrs Jolley,
'there is a book called Proverbs.

I'm going to read what it says
about ants.

"Lazy people should learn a lesson
from the way ants live,"' she read.

'I think we have a classroom of lazy people today.

You certainly don't look as busy as these ants.'

Mrs Jolley pointed to the vivarium.

'Ants are very hard-working. Each nest has a queen ant. She lays all the eggs.

These eggs become larvae and hatch into baby ants.

Most ants are worker ants. They look after the babies. They feed them and clean them.'

'Sounds just like Mum with Daniel,' said Rosie.

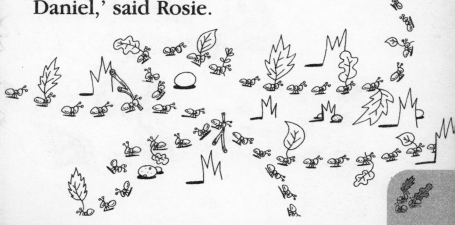

Mrs Jolley smiled at Rosie and
went on about the ants.

'Other worker ants leave the nest
to bring back food.

Ants keep their nests very clean
by taking away all the rubbish.

Now, I think we will all start again,'
said Mrs Jolley.

'Let's have lots of worker children!

Back to your seats,
and remember the ants.'

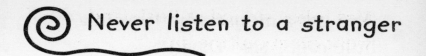

Never listen to a stranger

Mrs Jolley was in her chair and the children were on the story mat.

They were talking about animals.

Not wild and woolly jungle animals, but pets.

'I have a cat at home,' said Mrs Jolley. 'She jumps on my bed in the morning to wake me up.

I've had her since she was a kitten. Now she's quite old.

Tell me about your pets, please.'

'I've got a mouse who lives in a little cage,' said David.

'We've got a spotty dog,' said Rosie and Joshua together. 'He's a Dalmatian.'

'My tortoise lives in the garden,' said Sarah.

'My cat's black and white,' said Sam.

'Our dog's going to have puppies soon,' said Michael. 'She's ever so fat!'

'Have all your pets got names?'
asked Mrs Jolley.

'Our dog's called Spots,' said Rosie.

'My rabbit is called Honey,'
said Sarah. ''Cos Honey rhymes
with bunny.'

'My cat's called Winkle,' said Sam.

'Our dog's name is Sherbet,'
said Michael. 'But I don't know
what we'll call her puppies.'

'And my cat's called Paws,'
said Mrs Jolley.

The children laughed.

'I want to tell you a story that
Jesus told his friends.

It's a story about sheep.

Jesus told lots of stories
about sheep.

There were lots and lots of sheep
in the land where Jesus lived.

People only had to look at the hills
to see hundreds of sheep.

Can you tell me what we call
a man who looks after sheep?'
asked Mrs Jolley.

Hannah put up her hand.

'He's called a shepherd,' she said.

'Well done, Hannah,' said Mrs Jolley.
'Shepherds are very special people.

When Jesus told his story, shepherds
had a very hard and dangerous job.

Sheep could be chased by
wild animals.

There were wolves and even
bears on the hills.

The shepherd had to save his sheep
from these animals.

The shepherd gave each of his sheep a name.

The sheep knew their names.

When the shepherd called out their names, the sheep followed him — like your dog or cat comes when you call its name.

"But," said Jesus, "the sheep will not follow anyone else because they don't know his voice.'"

Mrs Jolley looked at all the children.

'I want to tell you something very important.

You must never, never go with anyone you don't know.

Even if a stranger calls your name, you must be like the sheep, and never follow him.'

41

Harvest

'Next week,' said Mrs Jolley,
'is our Harvest Festival.

We shall have a special
school assembly.'

'In the Big Hall with all the others?'
asked Emma.

'That's right,' said Mrs Jolley,
'all the school together.

Harvest is a thank-you time.
A thank-you for all the things
that God has given us.

If you can think of some of them,
I'll write a list.'

'Bananas!' said David.

'Apples,' said Hannah.

'Chips,' said James.

'I think I'll call that potatoes, James,' said Mrs Jolley as she wrote it down.

'Burgers,' said Michael.
'I love burgers.'

'And fish fingers,' added Rosie, ''specially with tomato sauce.'

'And lollies,' said Joshua.
'Big red lollies.'

'We should say "thank you" for food,' said Mrs Jolley.

'But what about other things?'

'Dogs!' said Michael.
''Specially my dog, Sherbet.'

'And my cat, Paws,' said Mrs Jolley.

'And Honey, my bunny,' said Sarah.

'Grandad,' said Sam, 'my grandad. I love my grandad.'

'And mums and dads,' said Rosie.

'We're getting a lovely long list,'
said Mrs Jolley.

'Now we need to think about
the assembly.

I want to read a few verses from
the Bible.

And afterwards I'll tell you why.

In the Bible there are 150 songs,
which we call Psalms.

I'm going to read from Psalm 65.

Shut your eyes. Now try to see
the picture the words are painting.

What a rich harvest your
goodness provides! Wherever
you go there is plenty. The
pastures are filled with flocks;
the hillsides are full of joy.
The fields are covered with
sheep; the valleys are full of
wheat. Everything shouts and
sings for joy.

What did you see in that picture?'

'I saw lots and lots of sheep,'
said Hannah.

'They were eating the grass
in the fields.'

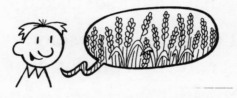

'I saw lots of corn growing,'
said David.

'And I saw lots of people,
all being happy!' said Rosie.

Everyone laughed at what Rosie said.

'Well done,' said Mrs Jolley.

'Now we are going to paint
that picture.

We'll make a great big frieze showing
the hills and valleys.

Everyone can make his or
her own sheep and then stick it
on the frieze.'

'Can I make a horse?' asked Hannah.

'Yes, I think we'll put some
horses and cows on our picture too,'
said Mrs Jolley.

The children went back to their seats
and started to make their sheep.

David, Sarah and Joshua helped
Mrs Jolley make the frieze.

'It will have to be a really big one,'
said Mrs Jolley.

'We shall put it up in the Big Hall
for the assembly.'

For the next few days the children
painted, cut and stuck.

David, Sarah and Joshua
finished the frieze.

Everyone came and stuck his
or her own sheep on it.

There were some horses and cows.

'There's no people,' said Sam.

'Well done, Sam,' said Mrs Jolley.

'But you are going to be the people.

In the assembly you are all going to stand in front of the frieze.

Everyone will say "thank you" for one thing.

That's why I made the list earlier.

So we'll start with David saying,
"Thank you for bananas."

Then when everyone has finished
I shall read those verses again.

And you will be the everyone who
shout and sing for joy.'

And that's what happened.

A week later, the Harvest Festival
assembly went very well indeed.

Sarah's a bridesmaid

Sarah came skipping into school
one Monday morning. She looked
very happy.

Mrs Jolley saw that Sarah was
looking happy.

'I'm going to be a bridesmaid,'
said Sarah. 'My big sister Charlotte
is getting wedded!'

'That's very exciting, Sarah,' said Mrs
Jolley. 'When is the wedding?'

'On Saturday,' said Sarah.
'I'm going to try on my bridesmaid's
dress after school.'

Sarah was very excited.

She talked to all her friends about the wedding.

Sarah got more and more excited as the wedding got nearer.

Mrs Jolley spoke to Sarah's mummy after school.

She asked if Sarah could do something rather special.

Sarah's mummy agreed.

Sarah had a big bag with her on
the Monday after the wedding.

All Sarah's friends kept asking her
what was in it.

'Secret!' said Sarah. 'It's a big secret.'

Mrs Jolley put the big bag in her
cupboard.

After play, the children sat on the story mat.

But there was someone missing.

It was Sarah.

'On Saturday,' said Mrs Jolley, 'Sarah's big sister got married.

Sarah was a bridesmaid.

And Sarah wore a special dress.'

There was a knock on the
classroom door.

The children looked to see
who it was.

'Come in,' said Mrs Jolley.

It was Sarah.

She was wearing her
bridesmaid's dress.

She looked very beautiful.

All the children clapped.

Sarah told everyone about
the wedding.

There was the service in church.

There were lots of photographs.

And then there was a big meal
with lots to eat.

Then there was a disco.

'It was like a party,' said Sarah.

'I didn't go to bed until after
ten o'clock!'

Sarah went off to change.

'I want to tell you a story about a wedding,' said Mrs Jolley.

'Jesus and his friends went to this wedding.

Mary, Jesus' mother, was there too.

Half-way through the wedding, she whispered something to Jesus.

"They've run out of wine," she said quietly.

Jesus wanted people to enjoy
the wedding.

He wanted everyone to be happy.

Jesus did something that only Jesus
could do.

He changed some big pots of water
into wine.

It was very good wine that
Jesus made.

Everybody said it was the best
they had tasted.

Jesus and his friends enjoyed the party.

The bride and bridegroom had a very happy day.

I wonder if they ever found out that Jesus helped to make it so happy.'

Sarah came back and sat down.

'Thank you, Sarah,' said Mrs Jolley.

'Thank you for sharing your happy day with us.'

Bible references and prayers

The Bible references for each story are given to enable the background of the story to be used if required. By their nature the stories are short, make one point, and omit much of the detail from the biblical passage. The stories can readily be the starting point for useful classroom discussion between the class teacher and the children. A prayer for each story theme is given. These prayers are based on the traditional approach of a response to the leader so that the children become involved in the prayers and make them their own.

Feet first
John 13:1–11

Loving Father,
Thank you for Jesus.
For the way he cares about us,
And shows us how to care.
When we haven't been helpful,
We are sorry.
When we think about ourselves first,
We are sorry.
When we forget to say sorry,
We are sorry.

A new school for Nathan
Genesis 12:1–7

Dear Jesus,
You know what it is like to leave home.
You left heaven and came to earth.
You left Nazareth to start your work.
For families moving to new homes,
Please be with them.
For old people giving up their homes,
Please be with them.
For those who have lost their homes because of war,
Please be with them.

I'm the best!
Luke 9:46–48

Heavenly Father,
Thank you for all the things we can do—
For running, jumping and skipping,
For painting, drawing and reading.
When we boast that we are best,
We are sorry.
When we think we are better than others,
We are sorry.
When we say unkind words about others,
We are sorry.

Follow the ants
Proverbs 6:6–11

Creator God,
Thank you for all the animals with which we
share your world.
Thank you for what we can learn from them.
For the busyness of ants,
Thank you.
For the love of our pets,
Thank you.
For the wonderful world we live in,
Thank you.

Never listen to a stranger
John 10:1–5

Dear Father,
You are always near us.
You love us very much,
And you keep us safe.
For those who care for us at home,
Thank you.
For those who care for us at school,
Thank you.
For the police, doctors and nurses,
Thank you.

Harvest

Psalm 65:9–13

Great God our Father,
You have made a beautiful world
for us to live in.
Help us to look after it.
For farmers who grow food for us,
Please be with them.
For those who look after animals,
Please be with them.
For those who have dangerous jobs,
Please be with them.
For those people who have bad harvests
and are hungry,
Please be with them.

Sarah's a bridesmaid

John 2:1–10

Jesus,
You lived on earth with a very happy family.
Help us to be happy by ourselves or with others.
For all those families who are unhappy,
Please be with them.
For families where someone is ill,
Please be with them.
For families who are having a party,
Please be with them.

Look out for five more 'On the Story Mat' books.
Also available: double cassette
including all 42 stories.